The Wise Bear Stories

Helping you through life's journey

Discovering your
own Uniqueness

Scott Cranfield

Illustration Raphilena Bonito

The Wise Bear Stories
Discovering your own Uniqueness
Scott Cranfield

Text and Illustration © Scott Cranfield

ISBN 9781912821037

A CIP catalogue record for this book
is available from the British Library.

Published 2019
Tricorn Books
Aspex Gallery, 42 The Vulcan Building
Gunwharf Quays
Portsmouth PO1 3BF

Printed & bound in the UK

The Wise Bear Stories

Discovering your own Uniqueness

How it Started:

Scott Cranfield the Author of Wise Bear has coached at the highest level for over 30 years, appearing on TV, radio, magazines, as well as hosting multiple seminars and being a key note speaker. His coaching covers subjects from life coaching and family relationships, to sport and business.

Since a young age I have been fascinated with and studied ways to help myself and others live the most inspired and fulfilled life possible. My journey has involved travelling the World attending countless programs and courses covering just about every area of life with the World's leading teachers.

As a father I wanted to share the best of what I had learnt with my children. I found a very effective way of doing this was through bedtime stories. I would create stories involving the challenges and anxieties my children had experienced that day and at the centre of each story is a character called Wise Bear. During the story the children would share with Wise Bear what was upsetting them or causing them to feel anxious. Wise Bear would use his vast experience and wisdom and share a whole new way of looking at these concerns to bring a calming balance to the children's mind, a balance they couldn't find on their own.

In each story the children learn useful tools and actions they can then apply for the rest of their lives.

My whole family are involved in bringing these stories to life, and it is our wish that these stories now help many other children and families, in the way they have helped ours.

Who is Wise Bear:

Wise Bear has been in the same family for generations. He has developed a unique wisdom that allows him to guide children, helping them dissolve their anxieties, as well as helping them make sense of the

different challenges and events they experience in their lives.
Every story covers a different subject, but within each story Wise Bear offers timeless lessons and vital life skills to help children navigate the journey of their life.

The lessons from Wise Bear will bring a calming balance to your children's mind, and give them a new and empowering perspective on any anxieties or challenges they face.

Even at 100 years old Wise Bear is still fascinated to learn and develop himself. He has had many brilliant teachers along the way, one special one he affectionately refers to as Dr D.

Wise Bear loves to read, exercise, make healthy smoothies and meditate. The only thing that gives away his age are some of his quirky sayings!

More than a story:
Each story ends with an affirmation and a short exercise to reinforce the lesson you have been reading about. This is a great opportunity to work with your children and help them apply the lessons directly to their own life.

Affirmations are a powerful way to develop strong and empowering beliefs for children, and the exercises give the children the opportunity to work through some of the challenges they face, so they can dissolve the anxieties and negative effects they hold in their mind.

Discovering your own Uniqueness

Christmas was approaching and Toby and Alex were feverish with excitement – it was their favourite time of the year. In addition, today was the last day of term at school and the school awards ceremony was being held. Mum and Dad were coming to watch and the children were eager to make them proud.

"Remember that story I wrote about time travel?" said Alex. "I really hope that I win a prize for that. If I win, I'd get a book token and I could go to the shops tomorrow and spend it!"

"Yeah, that was a good story. My teacher really liked my model of a castle. Do you think I might win a prize for that?" asked Toby, imagining himself walking up to receive his prize if his name was called out.

The ceremony began. As the afternoon went on, several of Toby and Alex's friends were called up to the stage to receive their prizes.

"Spelling Prize – Emily Evans!" called out Mrs Yates, the head teacher.

Everyone clapped. Emily's parents cheered and beamed proudly.

Meanwhile, Toby and Alex were on the edge of their seats, waiting for their names to be announced. But it wasn't to be. Neither of them had won a prize. They were very disappointed and were finding it hard to hide.

In the car on the way home both children were very quiet. They sat in the back, staring out of the window. Alex in particular looked sad.

"What's up, Alex?" asked Dad. He and Mum had had a good afternoon, celebrating the achievements of the students.

"I will never be as good as Emily."

"What do you mean?" quizzed Dad. "You're doing really well at school."

Alex wasn't really listening. Emily had received three awards during assembly.

"Emily is so good at everything. She is in the top set for maths and English, and she always comes first at sports day. I will never be as good as her," Alex blurted out. She slouched back into her seat.

They arrived back at the house and walked through into the living room. Wise Bear was standing precariously on a stool, reaching up high to put a colourful bauble near the top of the Christmas tree. The stool wobbled.

"Oh sausages!" muttered Wise Bear, as he managed to steady himself.

Dad chuckled to himself, but Alex was still looking miserable.

Dad walked over to Wise Bear, who was admiring his handiwork.

"Looking splendid, isn't it?" their furry friend said proudly.

Dad agreed enthusiastically, but Alex just sniffed grumpily.

"Alex, maybe Wise Bear could help you out? He might be able to help you see things in a new way," Dad said, putting his arm round his daughter.

Alex looked up, looking first at Dad and then at Wise Bear.

"Oh, OK," said Alex, not too sure about it. "I suppose we could try. But I don't know how it will help me be as good as Emily."

Alex looked up at Wise Bear, the Christmas tree lights twinkling behind him.

"Wise Bear, I don't think you can help," said Alex sadly.

"Well let's see, shall we. What is on your mind?" he replied, shaking his paws to release excess tension from stretching up to decorate the tree.

Alex launched into her sorry tale.

"I really wanted to get an award at assembly today, but I didn't. I thought I had done really well this term. My friend Emily won lots of awards. I don't think I will ever win anything," she said, barely taking time to breathe.

Wise Bear nodded sagely.

"Alex, come and sit down with me," he said comfortingly, plonking himself on the comfy chair and patting the bean bag next to him, encouraging Alex to sit.

Alex threw herself into the bean bag with a large whoosh.

"Do you remember a conversation we had about values and what is important to one person may not be important to another?"

Alex took a moment to think.

"Umm, only a little bit," said Alex quietly.

"Well, let me refresh your memory because it's important for the challenge you're faced with here.

"Whilst it is hard to believe, I want you to understand that nobody is actually any more intelligent or any more successful than another person, they just happen to have different things that are important to them."

"I don't understand," said Alex. "Emily is certainly a lot more clever than me and more successful in loads of things."

Wise Bear sighed and looked intently at Alex.

"That's only because you're comparing yourself to the things that Emily loves doing and forgetting the things you love doing.

"Remember Alex, even though you are at a great school they can't run lessons in every subject. This means that the things that you love doing may not be covered at school. So why don't we take a look to find out where your own intelligence and success is?"

Alex fidgeted in the bean bag, trying to get comfortable. She didn't think that she could ever compare to Emily.

"Alex, it is obvious to me that singing, dancing and drama are of high priority to you because you always have so much energy for them. And Mum and Dad never have to remind you to practise."

"That's true," said Alex, thinking about how much she loves performing.

"Does your school cover these subjects, Alex?" Wise Bear asked.

"They do a little bit," said Alex. "But not that much. I get to sing in the choir which I enjoy but that's not my favourite type of singing. That's why I go to the performing arts club at the weekend."

"And I believe you've been quite successful this year at these clubs?" encouraged Wise Bear.

Suddenly Alex sat up straight and became more animated. She started to smile.

"Well yes, I have taken two exams and I achieved distinction in them both. Also, I have been asked to sing two solos in shows this year and that is something I have never achieved before!"

Wise Bear could see Alex was thinking better, so he carried on.

"And where else have you been successful?" he prompted.

Alex thought for a moment.

"After the shows, other parents have come up to me to say how good I was on the stage and how I really stood out. So I guess that shows that I have been successful," said Alex.

Wise Bear could see these questions were really beginning to change the way Alex looked at herself, but he had a couple more important questions to ask her.

"Alex, what is Emily like at singing, dancing and drama?"

"Well, she is quite good at singing – she's in the choir – but I do know that she doesn't sing outside of school and she doesn't go to any drama clubs. And in the school play she does forget her lines quite a bit."

"And what are you like at remembering your lines," asked Wise Bear.

"Actually I remember them quite easily. In fact, very often the teacher uses me as an example of someone that remembers their lines. I even remember other people's lines!" Alex said proudly.

Wise Bear, sensing that Alex might be getting a little ahead of herself, moved on to the next very important lesson.

"Alex, I think you can already see that when you compare yourself to things that are important to others but maybe not so important to you, this can make you feel bad."

Alex nodded in agreement.

"Yet when you look at those things that are most important to you, you can see this is where you have success. However, this doesn't make you any better than someone else or them any better than you. What it shows you is that every person is unique with a different set of priorities, and that their success and intelligence will show up in their highest priorities."

Wise Bear noticed a frown come over Alex's face.

"Did I say that last part too fast?" he asked gently.

"Eh, yes. Not sure I followed that," said Alex.

"By Jove, yes it is a tendency of mine to speak a bit fast. I am sorry. Let me try saying it another way."

"When something is important to you – or you might say is of highest priority to you – you naturally want to learn more about it and spend more time doing it."

Alex thought for a moment. She did spend hours singing and not even notice the time going by.

Wise Bear continued.

"This often means you will get good at the things that are most important to you, and as a result you will appear intelligent or successful in this area – more so than someone who doesn't place the same importance or priority in that area." Wise Bear looked intently at Alex, his furry eyebrows twitching.

Alex thought for a moment, letting it sink in.

"Yes," she said decisively. "I am following you now."

Alex was now sitting forward on the bean bag, really listening and nodding her head to show she was understanding Wise Bear's lesson.

"Also, Alex, you said that you are good at remembering your lines for drama or singing shows?"

"Yes!" she replied.

"Well that is because your mind really does work differently when you are working on your highest priorities, and your memory improves."

"What do you mean?" she said, perplexed.

Wise Bear ran his paw through the chestnut fur on his head, making his right ear flap.

"When something is important to you, you will remember the information more easily. Yet when something is less important to you, you can easily forget the information. That's why you might remember your lines for a show and yet Emily will forget them, and Emily will remember a formula in maths, that you might forget.

"It isn't because one person has a good memory and the other person has a bad memory; you both have good memories, just linked to your highest priorities and what is important to you.

"So the lesson here, Alex, is to realise that every person is unique, and it is wise to be thankful for your own uniqueness and to build on that, rather than putting yourself down by comparing yourself to others!"

There was another part to this lesson Wise Bear wanted to share, which would help Alex, and others, get better at the things that aren't so important to them. But he knew this had taken quite a bit of thought for Alex, so he decided to hold back the lesson on linking those things that are of lower importance to the things that are high priority for another day.

Alex had a big smile on her face.

"Thank you, Wise Bear!" Alex said jumping up. "I think this is the most important lesson I have learnt from you. I really was feeling down on myself because I kept looking at what Emily was achieving and comparing myself to her which was making me feel sad. I never believed I could be as good as her in those subjects. But you are right, I am successful and I do have a good memory and I am smart in the things that I love doing."

Wise Bear grinned and clapped his paws – he loved it when his lessons were understood so clearly.

"I also now understand that no two people are the same and that we shouldn't try to be like someone else, but instead we should appreciate ourselves for the way we are and build on that."

By now, Alex was on her feet, twirling around as if she were on stage in one of her shows.

She spun round and gave Wise Bear a big hug and thanked him for his help. She then ran into the kitchen and gave Dad a big cuddle.

"Dad, thanks for asking me to speak to Wise Bear. He has really helped me."

Dad grinned and watched as Alex skipped to her room, singing contentedly.

Wise Bear Affirmation: What you say to yourself can make a big difference to how you think.
That's why Wise Bear always recommends an affirmation to help you remember his stories.
Here is today's one…

"I recognise and appreciate the uniqueness in myself and others"

Wise Bear recommends repeating these affirmations regularly. You can say them either out loud or inside your head.

Use the exercise below to discuss with your children and family how Wise Bear thinking can help you.

To help you grasp the lesson from this story, list below where you have had success. This can be in the form of certificates, medals and even compliments from others including teachers, family and friends. Try to list 10 separate examples where you know you have had success.

Here is one example to start you off:

The form of success: medals; compliments; reports; certificates etc.	Where did this feedback come from? School; clubs; family; friends etc.	The subject of my success; sports; academics; creativity; helping others; performing; making things; drawing etc.
School reports	School – various teachers	In my last 2 reports it said I have been excellent at looking out for and helping others.

The form of success: medals; compliments; reports; certificates etc.	Where did this feedback come from? School; clubs; family; friends etc.	The subject of my success; sports; academics; creativity; helping others; performing; making things; drawing etc.

The form of success: medals; compliments; reports; certificates etc.	Where did this feedback come from? School; clubs; family; friends etc.	The subject of my success; sports; academics; creativity; helping others; performing; making things; drawing etc.

To find out more about how Wise Bear links
things that are of lower importance to those
things that are higher importance read
'How To love the Things You Don't'